NOTE TO PARENTS

This familiar Bible story has been retold in a sensitive and simple way so that young children can read and understand it for themselves. But the special message of the story remains unchanged. It is the message of God's love and care for us all.

The Good Samaritan

retold by Marjorie Newman
illustrated by Edgar Hodges

Copyright ©MCMLXXXVIII by World International Publishing Limited.
All rights reserved.
Published in Great Britain by World International Publishing Limited.
An Egmont Company, Egmont House,
P.O. Box 111, Great Ducie Street,
Manchester M60 3BL.
Printed in DDR.
ISBN 7235 3008 4

Once a man wanted to get from Jerusalem to Jericho. He had no camel or donkey to ride. "I shall have to walk," he said to himself. And he trembled with fear, because it was very dangerous to walk from Jerusalem to Jericho.

He put on his clean clothes. He picked up a bag with his money in it. And all the time he felt very frightened.

The road was steep and rocky, and robbers often hid behind the rocks! The man set out. He hurried along, looking fearfully from right to left.

Suddenly – robbers sprang out!

The robbers knocked the man to the ground. They stole his clothes and his money. Then they ran off, leaving him lying by the roadside.

The poor man tried to get up, but he couldn't. His head hurt. His arms hurt. His legs hurt. He hurt all over. Would he die there, in the hot sun?

The man lay with his eyes shut. But then he heard something! Step ... step ... step ... Someone was coming down the road! Someone who might help! The poor man opened his eyes.

It was a priest! Surely a priest would help! Eagerly the man waited. And the priest saw him — but he crossed over, and walked by on the other side of the road.

The poor man couldn't believe it! He
groaned to himself. He felt very ill. Then he
heard more footsteps. He tried to lift his head
to see who was coming.

It was a minister of the Temple!
Surely a minister would help!

No. The minister crossed over, and he walked
by on the other side of the road. The poor
man lay back. Tears ran down his face.
Then ...

Clip, clop, clip, clop, clip, clop. What was that?

A man from a country called Samaria
was coming. A Samaritan. He was
leading a donkey.

The poor hurt man shut his eyes. It was no use expecting a Samaritan to help. He'd always been told that Samaritans were horrible people, and very unkind.

But the donkey's footsteps stopped.
The Samaritan came over to the poor man.
He didn't seem afraid that the robbers might
come back. "I'll help you," he said.
His voice was very kind.

The Samaritan bathed the poor man's
aching head. He put soothing oil on all the
bumps and bruises. "You can't stay here
by the roadside," he said.

"I can't walk," groaned the poor man.
"I can't even stand up."

"Don't worry," said the Samaritan.
"You can ride on my donkey."

Clip, clop, clip, clop, clip, clop. The donkey picked his way carefully over the stones.

"You're not well enough to go all the way to Jericho," said the Samaritan. "Rest at the inn with me. You may feel better in the morning."

That night, the Samaritan took care of the poor man. But in the morning, the man still wasn't better. "You must stay here until you're quite well," said the Samaritan.

"Wait a minute!" said the innkeeper.

"He hasn't any money! How is he going to pay me?"

"I'll pay you," said the Samaritan. He gave the innkeeper two pieces of silver. "If this isn't enough, I'll give you more money when I come next time," he said.

Soon the man was quite well. And he knew that not all Samaritans were horrible and unkind!

The first person to tell this story was Jesus. Someone asked him, "Who is my friend and neighbour?"

Jesus answered with the story of the Good Samaritan. "Which of those three men acted like a friend and neighbour?" he asked.

"The one who was kind to him," the people answered.

"Go – and do the same," said Jesus.

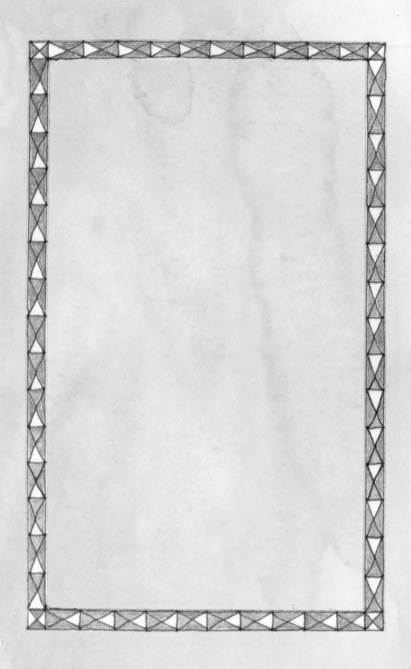